# VATNAJÖKULL

## ICE ON FIRE

ARI TRAUSTI GUÐMUNDSSON AND RAGNAR TH. SIGURÐSSON

# VATNAJÖKULL

## ICE ON FIRE

ARCTIC BOOKS

REYKJAVÍK
1996

# 1. VATNAJÖKULL

If you approach Iceland from the south by air or sea, the first sight to greet you will be Vatnajökull in all its glory, towering over the surrounding flatlands. Some might say it has a barren, even haughty appearance, but for others who see it slowly edging its way into view in the soft light of winter or the dazzling light of summer, it is extraordinarily beautiful and the first sign that they are home again.

Another approach, from the north through the highlands, renders an equally magnificent sight of the ice cap. On a clear day, its vast slopes and glaciers seem to spread halfway across the southern horizon, a magical kingdom of snow and ice, inviting and foreboding at the same time. Those who have ventured up onto the ice cap, and explored its reaches to a height of 1,000 metres or more have the same impression. Vatnajökull is a vast kingdom, divided from all that surrounds it, at once an ice palace and a white barren wasteland. From Skaftafell and the surrounding area, the ice cap with its high peaks, broad mountainous slopes and outlying glaciers looks like an alpine landscape. If one travels around it, there is still more variation to the landscape.

Eight times larger than its closest rival, Langjökull, the Vatnajökull ice cap creates a precipitation shadow over the surrounding lands to the north while at its southern border and nethermost reaches there is no protection at all from the snow and rain. During an average winter, 4 to 10 metres fall on the ice cap itself.

*The Vatnajökull ice cap is a remarkable natural phenomenon, rising to such a height that it controls the weather over large portions of the country. In the precipitation shadow of the central ice cap and of Mt. Öræfajökull lies one of the most beautiful areas in Iceland: the Skaftafell National Park and its environs.*

*Under this soft blanket of snow lies one of the largest volcanic centres in Iceland with a caldera some 600-700 metres deep. This is the Bárðarbunga volcanic centre. Little is known about its activity. A 415 m long ice core was drilled out of the glacier in 1972, which contained 30 layers of tephra and ice – the oldest dating from about 1650, but the ice core did not reach the bottom of the caldera.*

*The dimensions of the Vatnajökull ice cap appear even greater by moonlight. At Gríms-fjall there is a 40-50 metre direct line to Öræfajökull in the centre of the photograph. The Skaftafellsfjöll mountains lie below the moon.*

*Glacial ice is formed by a metamorphic process in snow subject to great pressure. This portion of the tongue of Breiðamerkurjökull could be up to 1,000 years old.*

## 2. ICE CAP RATHER THAN GLACIER

In geological terms, Vatnajökull is classified as an ice cap rather than as a glacier. The classification dates back to Sveinn Pálsson, Surgeon General of Iceland, and the country's leading pioneer in glaciological research at the end of the eighteenth century. The Vatnajökull ice cap is mainly broad and flat. Unlike alpine glaciers, it does not only cover steep slopes, nor does it spread out from converging ice-aprons like the valley glaciers found in mountainous regions in Scandinavia, the Alps, the Andes or the Himalayas. Instead, like all ice caps, it

covers a very wide area comprising of mountains, valleys and high plateaux in a blanket-like manner, where only a few peaks stand up out of it like skerries or islands in a solid white ocean. Its surface is convoluted in many places, in some areas with what look like huge white waves and in others by smaller ripples hinting at the landscape that lies buried beneath it. It is extremely thick, and many smaller glaciers extend from above the snowline on the main ice cap far down into the surrounding plains or into valleys at its outskirts.

The main or central ice cap lying above the snowline is sometimes called the firn area since this is where a good deal of the snow that falls in the winter remains until the following autumn. The snowline is usually found at a height of about 1,100-1,250 metres, but varies in different places on the ice cap and from year to year. Below it the winter snow disappears as does part of the ice lying beneath it. The firn area of Vatnajökull covers thousands of square kilometres, where freshly fallen snow soon turns to ice under its own weight. The ice then sinks and spreads out at the same time and moves slowly forward in the form of glaciers which begin to melt. The meltwater becomes part of the complex fresh water cycle in the northern hemisphere.

## 3. AMONG THE GIANTS OF THE NON-POLAR REGIONS.

In the polar regions proper, such as Greenland and Antarctica are huge ice caps, but outside those regions ice caps the size of Vatnajökull are a rare phenomenon. For example, Jostedalsbreen in Norway is similar in type but

*Polar regions in Iceland? A reflection of Greenland? People who venture onto the ice cap are often surprised at the diversity of the landscape up there. This photograph was taken at the edge of Kálfafellsdalur, a short distance from the Glacier Tours' service base.*

*The advent of specially built jeeps with oversized tires, from which the air could be partially released, caused a revolution in ice cap travel. These vehicles are fitted with a GPS positioning system and telecommunications equipment.*

*Vatnajökull and Öræfajökull give the south-east coast a unique appearance and are visible from far out at sea. Travellers come here to enjoy watching the whales. Here, a humpback whale is playing in a promotion film on glacial tours and whale watching.*

much smaller than either the Vatnajökull ice cap, the Hielo Sur or Hielo del Norte in Patagonia, Chile. Conversely, the polar ice caps on Ellesmere Island, the Novaya Zemlja off the Siberian coast and the Nord-Austlandet ice cap on Svalbard are larger than Vatnajökull. Greenland is covered by about 1.8 million square kilometres of ice (some 220 times the size of Vatnajökull) an area also referred to as an ice cap, but the complex system of glaciers and floating ice shelves in Antarctica, which covers an area of 13 million square kilometres, is harder to categorise under this title. In comparison, Vatnajökull is almost dwarfish. Yet it

is by far the largest ice cap in Europe, the largest in the northern hemisphere outside the polar region and one of the largest in any temperate area in the world. With a total area of about 8,300 square kilometres, it covers some 8 per cent of Iceland.

Vatnajökull represents a large proportion of southeast Iceland. It is almost 140 kilometres long, stretching from Tungnaárjökull in the west to Öxarfellsjökull in the east, and between 45-80 kilometres broad from north to south. Most of the ice cap stands at between 900-1,500 metres high, but at such places as

*The most prominent peak in the Skaftafjöll range is an old volcanic neck made of columnar basalt. It is called Þumall (1,279 m), which means "the thumb," and was first climbed in 1975. West of Þumall, especially at Kjós, are some geological formations consisting of light-coloured acid eruptive rock. They are part of the ruins of volcanic centre which is several million years old. Öræfajökull can be seen in the distance, and Miðfellstindur (1,430 m) to the right.*

Grímsfjall and Kverkfjöll it towers some 1700-1900 metres above sea level. Its highest points are at Bárðarbunga (2,000 metres) and Öræfajökull (2,119 metres). A few individual peaks and ranges project upwards out of the ice cap, for example at Goðahryggur in the east and Pálsfjall in the west, and there are large nunataks at Esjufjöll and Mávabyggðir in the south. At Esjufjöll, ninety individual types of vascular plants have been identified, and the area is a favourite nesting spot for several species of birds. The fauna and flora found on the ice cap are of the same type that existed in coastal areas during the last Ice Age.

*The ptarmigans need have no fear of being hunted in the Skaftafell National Park, and are therefore relatively tame.*

9

*Hardy plants can be found growing at 600-1,200 metres above sea level in many areas close to Vatnajökull and sometimes even on the ice cap itself, for example at the glacial peaks in Esjufjöll. Here, meltwater nourishes the pyramidal saxifrage at a height of 650 m near Skálafellsjökull.*

*Öræfajökull is actually a part of the Vatnajökull ice cap. Its highest point is Hvannadalshnúkur (2,119 m). The are three main routes to the summit: from the south over Hnappavellir, up over Virkisjökull and Hvannadalshryggur and, finally, the Sandfell route. It takes about 10-14 hours to reach the top. Behind the peak here is a snow plain which is actually an ice-filled caldera, some 500 m deep.*

At its thickest, ice cover of Vatnajökull is at least 900 metres deep, but its average thickness is closer to 400 metres. Most of the ice cap has been measured for thickness with Icelandic radio echo technology which uses electomagnetic waves. Its total volume is at least 3,320 cubic kilometres, weighing about 3,200 billion tons. At an average rate of discharge, it would take the powerful Ölfusá River more than 300 years to carry all the ice cap's meltwater to the sea, and over 1,000 substantial glacial bursts in Skeiðará would carry about an equal volume of water – the same as 16 million oil tankers each with a capacity of 200 thousand tons.

## 4. FIRE BENEATH THE SURFACE

To the west, the north and the northeast, there are only a few peaks that stand in the way of the ice cap's spread, while to the south there is a high but narrow range of mountains. One of them, the giant Öræfajökull, is volcanic and towers head and shoulders over all the other peaks in the area. It erupted in 1362 and 1727, and the earlier eruption was one of the most powerful in historical times. There are other large volcanoes hidden under the ice of Vatnajökull such as Grímsvötn, and towards the edges fissure swarms spread in opposite directions from each of these volcanic centres. There is an area of eruptive fissures connected to Grímsvötn, including Lakagígar, and a long and narrow volcanic system centred at Bárðarbunga which can be seen at Dyngjuháls and Vatnaöldur or Veiðivötn. North from Kverkfjöll is a bifurcated trunk of volcanic tuff formations and recent lava emissions. This is the northern part of the volcanic system with its powerful centre at the Kverkfjöll volcano. Southwest of Grímsvötn is the central volcano at

*There are many volcanic centres under Vatnajökull. It is known for certain that about 60 eruptions have taken place there over the last 1,100 years, and Grímsvötn is considered to be the most active volcanic system. The eruption that occurred about 5 km north of Grímsvötn in 1996 had its source in the near-by volcanic system of Bárðarbunga. This is the middle ice cauldron, where magma from the new eruption penetrated the ice cap.*

11

*From Kverkfjöll. High up in the central volcano of Kverkfjöll is the geothermal area of Hveradalur. This area has a potential power of 1,500-2,000 MW, but it will probably never be harnessed, partly because the area is too remote to be utilised, but also because it has become such an important tourist site. There are some large and impressive ice caves in the immediate vicinity. Kverkfjöll has erupted in historical times.*

Þórðarhyrna, and southwest of Bárðarbunga is yet another volcano of the same kind, known as Hamarinn. There are calderas at most of the central volcanoes which are 10-80 square kilometres in size, some of them reaching depths of up 600-700 metres.

This means that the whole of the western section of the ice cap is within the active volcanic belt, while the eastern section overlies bedrock formed 2-7 million years ago. This section is generally characterised by volcanoes which have been extinct for a very long time. The heat and geothermal energy beneath Vatnajökull give it a special status among the world's ice caps. There are various large and active volcanoes elsewhere which are covered with snow or glacial ice, but nowhere is there such a thick ice cap containing such enormous volcanic activity.

## 5. FREQUENT UNREST

The divergent plate margins in Iceland lie mainly to the west of Vatnajökull with their periodic and local rifting and their slow upwelling of magma. The volcanic systems

mentioned above and seven central volcanoes lie beneath the ice cap, while the centre of the Iceland hot spot (mantle plume), which supplies additonal magma, is to be found under the northwestern corner of the ice cap. All this indicates extensive volcanic activity. We know of 63 eruptions on or under Vatnajökull in historical times and suspect that there have been at least another 13-15 additional ones. This and the geothermal heat that accompany it lead to glacial bursts (floods), and the entire area is the site of seismic activity. Violent convulsions and volcanic unrest have always been common throughout the ages. Eruptions and earthquakes often occur in series, such as the famous Krafla Fires (in northeast Iceland) in 1975-84.

Occasionally the central volcanoes erupt directly from their magma chambers in the crust, or violent volcanic activity occurs in the systems' outlying fissures, under the ice cap or on unglaciated land. Rifting and eruptions occurred under the ice cap at Bárðarbunga and at Veiðivötn, which are part of the same system, in the late 15th century. As many as seven such eruptions took place at Grímsvötn

*Skeiðará has its source at the southeastern edge of Skeiðarárjökull, at the mouth of the Morsárdalur valley. It usually carries meltwater from the ice glacier discharging 100-150 $m^3$ metres per second. At intervals of several years, part of Grímsvötn empties into the river due to geothermal melting of the glacier ice. Then the river increases the discharge to 2,000-5,000 $m^3$ per second, as is the case here (April 1996). The discharge from the whole glacier can double in volume if there is an eruption either in or close to Grímsvötn which leads to a glacial burst.*

*Strange light reflected against elusive fog changes the ordinary surroundings of the National Park into a mysterious and magical place.*

in the 17th century, and when the nearby Lakagígar craters erupted in 1783-4, there occurred one of the most powerful lava eruptions the world had seen for a thousand years. Long spates of eruptions conncected to Bárðarbunga occurred from 1697-1729 and caused glacial bursts that poured into the River Jökulsá á Fjöllum. At least eight or nine eruptions are known to have taken place in the 19th century, and there were a number of lava eruptions north of Jökulheimar, at Tröllagígar from 1862-64. Early this century, there were eruptions at Bárðarbunga, Þórðarhyrna and Grímsvötn, and this last named volcanic centre also erupted again in 1922, 1934 and 1983.

In addition to the above, there have been numerous eruptions, for example in Grímsvötn and at Lokahryggur, which lies between Grímsvötn and Hamarinn. At Lokahryggur there are ice cauldrons above a subglacial ridge, and from beneath them water has surged into the River Skaftá over twenty times in the last four decades, usually as a result of geothermally melted ice. These glacial bursts, however, pale into insignificance in comparison to the enormous bursts that took place in Jökulsá á Fjöllum, Skjálfandafljót and Skeiðará due to volcanic eruptions from time to time. Smaller bursts in Skeiðará are caused when geothermal activity

at the main volcanic centre in Grímsvötn melts the surrounding ice. Water collects in a caldera lake beneath a 250 metre thick ice shelf that floats on its surface. This geothermal activity varies from century to century, as does the thickness of the ice. Geothermal activity at Grímsvötn has been diminishing for a while, and the caldera lake is currently about 10 square kilometres in area and about half a cubic kilometre in volume (i.e. 500 million cubic metres). Usually, when the lake reaches a certain level, the water forces its way slowly under the solid ice above the eastern rim of the caldera and then runs under Skeiðarárjökull into the River Skeiðará at 4-5 year intervals, at a volume of one cubic kilometre (a billion tons) and a rate of 2,000-5,000 cubic metres per second. When this happens, the floating ice shelf has risen by dozens of metres and the lake increases in size to about 20 square kilometres. Such glacial bursts continue for days on end, then the floating ice shelf sinks and breaks up. The bridges and roads on Skeiðarásandur stood up quite well to the enormous weight and pressure of the latest glacial burst of this type in April, 1996.

*A view from Hverdalur in Kverkfjöll across Dyngjujökull to Dyngjufjöll and Askja. The last volcanic activity in Kverkfjöll, which produced a relatively small eruption, occurred in 1959. There is a man standing on the small peak top right.*

*Most of the Skaftafell National Park can be seen in one glance from Skeiðarársandur. The Skaftafellsjökull glacier is at the centre and Öræfajökull to the right. This lake and the fertile area that surrounds it disappeared under the black sand and mud that was sweet along by the glacial burst in November, 1996.*

*In winter Jökulsárlón glacier lagoon freezes over. It is over 160 m deep and about 11 km² in area. It increases in size every year.*

When there is considerable volcanic activity at Grímsvötn or its environs, a huge volume of water runs into the caldera lake over a short period of time. The ice shelf can be lifted dozens of metres above its usual run-off level, and when that occurs the water rarely manages to create a channel of flow in sufficient time. Then the caldera lake increases to about 30-40 square kilometres and can contain as much as 3-5 cubic kilometres of water. Eventually, the deep water simply lifts the solid ice, bores its way underneath it, and speeds along its normal route beneath Skeiðarárjökull to converge with other outflows on Skeiðarársandur. A few cubic kilometres of water are thus carried forward at a rate 20,000-50,000 cubic metres per second. These larger glacial bursts carry hundreds of millions of tons of clay and sand out onto the plains and into the ocean. The flow breaks up the margins of the ice cap and huge icebergs are carried along the path of the flood. The various road sections and bridges on

*A view of Stigárjökull, one the smallest outlet glaciers branching out of Öræfajökull. On the right is Stigafoss (138 m), the second highest waterfall in Iceland. In the foreground are small step-like formations created by soil creeping along the slope.*

*Mountaineers in front of the Falljökull ice-fall, which is actually a branch of Virkisjökull leading from Öræfajökull.*

Skeiðarársandur were not constructed to withstand the largest glacial bursts.

## 7. VATNAJÖKULL IS THE CORRECT NAME

Vatnajökull stretches its branches in all directions in the form of slow moving outlet glaciers. Some of these are wide and flat with an ice velocity of approximately 10-15 centimetres a day. Others are steep and narrow, and can move at a rate of over one metre a day. The ice velocity is determined partly by the water level under the ice cap, and much of Vatnajökull is made up of temperate glacier ice (0°C). All these outlet glaciers retreat when precipitation is low or when the air temperature increases. At such times, too little ice moves along into the outlet glaciers. Conversely, heavy precipitation and cold weather cause the outlet glaciers to advance slowly but surely. If we include the Öræfajökull glaciers, there are thirty six outlet glaciers on Vatnajökull. Rivers flow from all of them, the largest of which have a mean annual discharge of 100-300 cubic metres per second. Among the best known of these rivers are Skeiðará, Jökulsá á Dal (or Brú), Lagarfljót, Jökulsá á Fjöllum, Skjálfandafljót and Tungnaá. In addition to this last

named river, the Þjórsá River at Hofsjökull, dams and reservoirs supply water to the largest hydropower plants in Iceland. Thus Vatnajökull is at the hub of the nation's power complex.

Many marginal glacial lagoons border the outlet glaciers of the ice cap. The largest of these are Grænalón, on the western perimeter of Skeiðarárjökull, and Jökulsárlón at Breiðamerkurjökull. The former is the source of glacial bursts in Súla which occur when so much water collects in the lagoon that it floods its banks. The latter is best known for its boat tours among the majestic icebergs that float on its surface. There is only a short distance from Jökulsárlón to the ocean, where the currents of the Atlantic Ocean almost flood directly into the lagoon. Ice depth measurements have revealed a 20 kilometre long valley beneath Breiðamerkurjökull, and it is thus possible that the lagoon may change into an ice fjord over the next few decades. All the broad and flat outlet glaciers of the ice cap rush forward regularly, at intervals of approximately 30-100 years. This movement is generally referred to as a glacial surge. For some reason these outlet glaciers do not carry new ice deposits forwards and downwards at a sufficient rate between surges and an imbalance is

*Unlike the slopes and crevasses on the Falljökull glacier, Tungnaárjökull (approx. 130 km² ) is relatively smooth and flat. It is typical of the larger and broader outlet glaciers of the Vatnajökull ice cap. Like them, Tungnaárjökull is a surging glacier, which rushes forward every 40-50 years. When that occurs the surface of the ice cap can become quite rough, as can be seen here (1995).*

*During a glacial surge in 1995, Tungnaár-jökull pushed up layers of ice on a small lagoon. The muddy flow at the margin suggests that water plays a part of the fast surge, moving ice some 10-20 metres per day.*

*The glacial surge of Tungnaárjökull in 1995. Creavesse patterns like this are common where the ice overrides hills in the redrock or on top of the ice waves that travel towards the margin during the surge.*

created between the upper and lower parts of their glacial tongues. The glaciers then become very steep, and large waves are formed which move suddenly forward and make the surface convulse until the whole glacier begins to follow suit and move at a rate of 10-100 metres a day, and from 1-10 kilometres all in all. For example, Dyngjujökull, Brúarjökull and Síðujökull surged in the sixties and Tungnarárjökull in the fifties. In 1994-96, Skaftárjökull and Sylgjujökull surged forward along with Tungnaárjökull and Síðujökull (all of which are situated in the western part of the ice cap) with such force that one could hear the sound of them moving, and water broke out from many places at the ice margin. This indicates that the waterways within the ice are subject to change and that water manages to flow to some extent under the whole surface of the moving outlet glacier as it makes it way forward at great speed.

## 8. AN EVENTFUL TALE

It is difficult to find clear evidence concerning the formation and history of Vatnajökull. Unfortunately, documentary evidence is

parse and actual physical traces have often been quickly destroyed by the ice cap itself or by various rivers and lakes. However, general changes in temperature and precipitation over the last thousand years do provide us with clues about the glacial budget. The first thing to note is that the last Ice Age came to a close in Iceland about 9,000 years ago. We can assume that there have always been some glaciers on the highest mountains during the entire interglacial period which commenced at that time and which continues to the present day. There have been two warm periods during that stretch of time: the first about 7,000-9,000 thousand years ago and the second about 2,500-4,500 years ago. The highest peaks on Vatnajökull were almost certainly covered by glaciers at that time. During a colder period, some 4,500-7,000 years ago, the glaciers were much more extensive but we know virtually nothing about them.

It was thus about 2,000-2,500 years ago that the weather began to cool again, and greater precipitation meant a positive glacial budget. It was then that the Vatnajökull ice cap began to increase in size. Small, individual ice caps in the highlands began to converge both in the valleys and on the high plateaux, but we do not know when Vatnajökull actually merged together into one whole nor what it looked like during the Settlement of Iceland (9th century). One thing, however, is clear: Vatnajökull was considerably smaller in the

*Síðujökull surged forward in 1994 by a distance of 1-2 km. The glacier has an area of 320 km², carrying well over 100 billion tons of ice. Gigantic ice towers were tumbling at the margin of the ice cap. They make the helicopter seem very small in comparison.*

*B*oat trips among the floating ice on Jökulárslón and past the margin of Breiðamerkurjökull are extremely popular. The opening sequence of the James Bond movie, "A View to a Kill," was shot here in 1984.

*T*here are few spots that afford such an excellent view as Hotel Skaftafell in Freysnes, close to Svínafell in Öræfi. The peaks of Hrútsfjallstindar (left) are nearly 1,900 m high and very popular among climbers. Hvannadalshnúkur (right) provides an easier route to the top. Alaskan lupins are planted to reclaim land in the old river bed of the Skeiðará.

*A* cold buffet at 1,250 m high on the ice cap. Many travellers feel that the long journey is well worth it when there are such delights to be enjoyed.

irst centuries after the Settlement than it is oday. During the cold period from 1300-900 (the Little Ice Age), the glaciers ncreased in size and extended farther than hey did in the first cold period. For example, round 1900 Breiðarmerkurjökull lay where here is now a bridge over the River Jökulsá. Ve can estimate that the tongues of the ancient ice cap moved forward by about 5-15 kilometres. New glaciers were formed and water poured out onto the fertile lands. The name Vatnajökull, which means "river glacier," probably derives from the time of the Little Ice Age, when it discharged such vast quantities of water. The names Klofajökull ("cloven glacier") and Austurjökull ("eastern

*A quiet evening at Vatnajökull, which has almost disappeared in the still mist. Horna- fjörður is not actually a fjord but part of the mouth of the River Hornafjarðarfljót and the site of Höfn. Höfn is a small but lively town and one of the central bases for tourist opera- tors who offer trips up onto the ice cap and into hiking areas like Lónsöræfi.*

*Trips of various lengths by snowcat, snow-mobile and jeep give the public a unique opportunity for adventure on the Vatnajökull ice cap.*

*Members of the Icelandic Glaciological Society measuring accumulation on Vatnajökull. An ice core, many metres in length, is drilled out of the snow during the winter. This is used to measure the thickness of the snow and its specific weight so that scientists can determine how many millimetres of water have been added to the ice mass as snow. In an average year most areas accrue 2,500-5,000 millimetres of water.*

glacier") referred sometimes to parts of the ice cap and sometimes to the entirety. The distances from ice divides to the borders are nowhere very great, and judging from the probable ice velocity, we can deduce that the oldest ice at the margins of the large glaciers of Vatnajökull are closer to 1,000 than 2,000 years old.

## 9. A PLAYGROUND FOR SCIENTISTS AND TRAVELLERS

In the past, very few people ventured either onto or across the ice cap, so that most of the place names have derived from this century. One of the easternmost peaks of Öræfajökull was first climbed in the 18th century, and the summit of Hvannadalshnúkur was not conquered until the 19th century. The first recorded expedition across the ice cap occurred in 1875. In that year a Briton, W.L.Watts, and his Icelandic companions travelled past Grímsvötn without noticing it, and it remained undiscovered until two Swedes reached it in 1919. There were several expeditions onto the ice cap in the 1930s on skis, but it was not until after the Second World War that the first traction-driven snowmobiles and snowcats were used. The

*O*utlet glaciers and peaks on Vatnajökull are regared as playgrounds by many visitors, and especially for those who have crampons and carry ice axes. Árni Árnason and his teddy bear ascend the steep ice at Hólarjökull on Öræfajökull.

*T*he walking routes through Lónsöræfi are among the most interesting in Iceland. The longest of these is from Lón to Snæfell, which takes about 4-5 days. There are regular jeep trips from Höfn to Lónsöræfi and other trips are operated by touring and hikers' clubs.

*T*here are numerous ice caves both in Vatna- jökull and at its margins. This cave is situated in an old layer of firn beside Skálafellsjökull, and was formed by meltwater. Other ice caves can be found at Grímsfjall, Kverkfjöll and Eyjabakkajökull.

*T*he Öræfajökull volcano is seldom more splendid a sight than when the northern lights (aurora borealis) dance above it in the sky. The red streaks are car headlights and indicate the length of the exposure. The northern lights occur when electrons, especially from the sun, gather together in the Earth's magnetic field and are drawn towards its surface until they begin to clash with molecules in the atmos- phere. Then energy is released in the form of light.

*Many of the shorter walking routes through the Skaftafell National Park pass well known natural phenomena such as Svartifoss. This waterfall is framed like a painting in an extremely dark basalt frame. It takes about thirty minutes to walk from the service centre along a marked path.*

*A few dozen farms lie in front of the southern margin of Vatnajökull, most of them quite some distance from the ice cap itself. One such farm is Núpsstaður, which has an ancient turf church and a timber farmhouse in the style popular in the early part of this century.*

*At Jökulsárlón in the cool night air of summer, the quiet solitude and magnificence of the landscape is more obvious than perhaps anywhere else in the country. Iceland's largest volcano stands in the background.*

Iceland Glaciological Society was founded in 1950 to carry out exploration and research on the ice cap. Such expeditions are still being carried by the IGS in cooperation with scientific institutes in Iceland. International research also takes place on Vatnajökull. It is mainly confined to glacial budgeting, and provides crucial information concerning past and present climatic changes. The advent of special jeeps with large tires and modern motorised sleds made much of the ice cap significantly more accessible, so that many travellers can now go up onto it with relative ease. There are excellent walking routes in the eastern part, especially at Lónsöræfi. In the west, at Skálafelsjökull, a service center has been built that offers snowmobile tours across magnificent areas of the ice cap. Thousands of travellers stop at Breiðamerkursandur, the home of the Great Skua, and visit the marvels of the Jökulsárlón lagoon by boat. But the most popular site is the Skaftafell National Park – one of the most impressive national parks in Europe. There are many fine walks to tempt all types of travellers, from short routes through the beautiful countryside to Svartifoss to guided trips across the ice cap led by

## 10. THE AWAKENING

On the 29th September, 1996, powerful earthquakes took place underneath Bárðarbunga. The quake centres moved southwards and tremors that accompany a flow of magma within the crust were also detected by monitoring devices. The following day, volcanic tremors were recorded on nearby seismographs. Closer observation revealed two ice cauldrons in the ice cap between Bárðarbunga and Grímsvötn-the same location as the eruption of 1938. It was clear that an eruption had started in a fissure about 4 kilometres long which lay from north to south at the foot of the Bárðarbunga volcano. A meandering channel with a partly sunken roof lay from the ice cauldrons towards Grímsvötn, along which gushed 4,000-5,000 tons of water per second. News of the eruption went all around the world. Magma, at a temperature of about 1,100°c

expert mountaineers. One can even take a sightseeing trip by plane. Many thousands of visitors also arrive each year to see the extraordinary geothermal area of Kverkfjöll at the north edge of the ice cap.

*Öræfi, especially Breiðamerkursandur, is the home of the Great Skua. An agile flier, this large and easily recognised bird is also known for its aggressive behaviour. This area contains the largest nesting grounds of the Great Skua in the North Atlantic.*

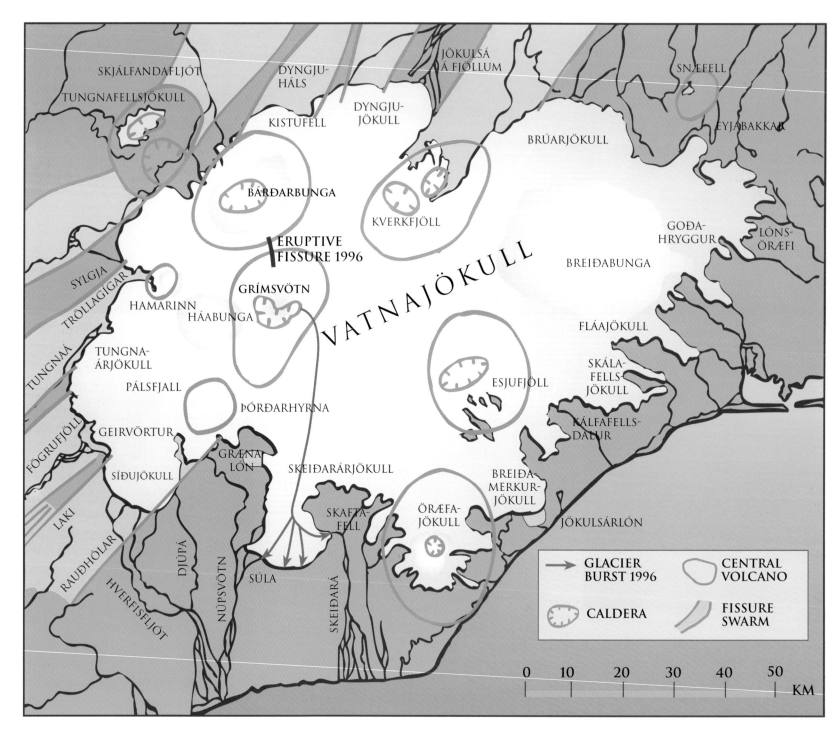

SKJÁLFANDAFLJÓT

TUNGNAFELLSJÖKULL

DYNGJU-HÁLS

JÖKULSÁ Á FJÖLLUM

SNÆFELL

DYNGJU-JÖKULL

KISTUFELL

EYJABAKKAR

BRÚARJÖKULL

BÁRÐARBUNGA

KVERKFJÖLL

GOÐA-HRYGGUR

LÓNS-ÖRÆFI

ERUPTIVE FISSURE 1996

BREIÐABUNGA

SYLGJA

TRÖLLAGÍGAR

GRÍMSVÖTN

HAMARINN

HÁABUNGA

V A T N A J Ö K U L L

FLÁAJÖKULL

TUNGNAÁ

TUNGNA-ÁRJÖKULL

SKÁLA-FELLS-JÖKULL

PÁLSFJALL

ESJUFJÖLL

ÞÓRÐARHYRNA

GEIRVÖRTUR

KÁLFAFELLS-DALUR

FÖGRUFJÖLL

GRÆNA-LÓN

SÍÐUJÖKULL

SKEIÐARÁRJÖKULL

BREIÐA-MERKUR-JÖKULL

LAKI

SKAFTA-FELL

ÖRÆFA-JÖKULL

JÖKULSÁRLÓN

RAUÐHÓLAR

DJÚPÁ

NÚPSVÖTN

SÚLA

HVERFISFLJÓT

SKEIÐARÁ

| | GLACIER BURST 1996 | | CENTRAL VOLCANO |
| --- | --- | --- | --- |
| | CALDERA | | FISSURE SWARM |

0    10    20    30    40    50

KM

*Three geophysicists from the University of Iceland at work. From the left: Páll Einarsson, Bryndís Brandsdóttir and Magnús Tumi Guð-mundsson. Seismograph readings indicated both the opening of the volcanic fissures and the steady stream of magma flowing from it.*

was breaking its way through the 450 metre thick ice cap over the palagonite (tuff) ridge that was formed in 1938. On the morning of October 2nd, the first black tephra was emitted from the northernmost of the two the ice cauldrons.

The magma was rapidly cooled in the water, and turned into dark granules spewed into the air by steam explosions and gases coming up from beneath the white surface of the ice and snow. Columns of tephra stood 300-500 metres high, and ash was carried even higher by eruptive clouds and driven to the northern and eastern parts of the country. Huge clouds of steam, between 12-14 kilometres high, were lifted by the power of the

eruption. While this was taking place, the fissure had lengthened by some two kilometres and a new ice cauldron appeared to the north in the 600-700 metre thick ice cap. There was a massive eruption underneath the ice, but yet not powerful enough to break all the way through. Close to the fissure, the ice was coloured brown and black by the tephra. People flew out to see the sight from the air and foreign journalists flocked to Iceland in droves.

The surface of the subglacial lake at Grímsvötn rose by about 5-10 metres a day at first, and it was thought that this would lead to a glacial burst in matter of a few days. That proved not to be the case, and as

*By September 30th, 1996, the eruption at Bárðarbunga had sunk two cauldrons, lying 400-500 metres deep, into the ice cap. The form of the subglacial channel through the ice cap can be seen behind the southern cauldron, leading towards the Grímsvötn caldera which contains a sub-glacial lake (far left).*

result there was time to prepare for the inevitable floods across Skeiðarársandur. Weather conditions were seldom favourable for close observation of the eruption site, but it was clear that the eruption was sizeable and that it was coming from the cauldron that was formed over the middle of the fissure. The andesitic material emitted, akin to that found at Hekla, was thought to issue

*The eruption began to slow down somewhat after the first week and the burning hot magma beneath the third and northernmost cauldron did not make its way through the ice cap. On October 12, the roof of the water channel leading from the middle cauldron had already collapsed (to the right).*

*After the eruption was over, the water flow from the active areas diminished considerably. This is a view down into the ice canyon, which is about 150 metres deep. November 4: the ice bridge has collapsed but the ice flow and snow will probably seal up this huge gorge within a year (ATG).*

*L*ooking down across Skeiðarárjökull towards Skeiðarsandur. The Skaftafell mountains lie to the left and the peaks of Súlutindar to the right. Underneath, water runs out of Grímsvötn to a distance of 50 km across the sands.

*N*ovember 4: a helicopter expedition of four men landed on the sandy margin at the crater's edge, most of which is covered by the ice cap and water in the central crater. The team comprised of Ómar Ragnarsson, Ragnar Axelsson, Sigmundur Arthúrsson and Ari Trausti Guðmundsson, who erected an Icelandic flag on this newly formed land, duly inscribed with their names.

*The evening sun breaks its way through the tephra covered pillow lava being emitted from the volcano. October 5: glacial eruptions usually form pillow lava, tephra and steam as water flows into the volcanic vents (ATG).*

*The central cauldron at the main eruption site on November 5, during the Skeiðará glacier burst. The circular area in the foreground is the crater, its rim torn apart by flowing water leaving two "islands." The helicopters landed on the shore of the western island on the right.*

*T*he outlet in the River Gígja early in the morning on November 5. This was one of the main pathways of the glacial burst and broke a huge channel into the glacier.

*T*he eastern margin of Skeiðarárjökull and Skaftafellsfjöll. The flood has almost reached its peak discharge, and the River Skeiðará is flowing at a rate of 10,000-15,000 m³ per second. The dark patches indicate where the flood water has broken up the surface of the ice cap.

*T*he bed of the River Gígja, where the bridge spanning it and the national highway once were. The flow of water reached well over 10,000 m³ per second and carried huge boulders of ice along with it. A view of Lómagnúpur.

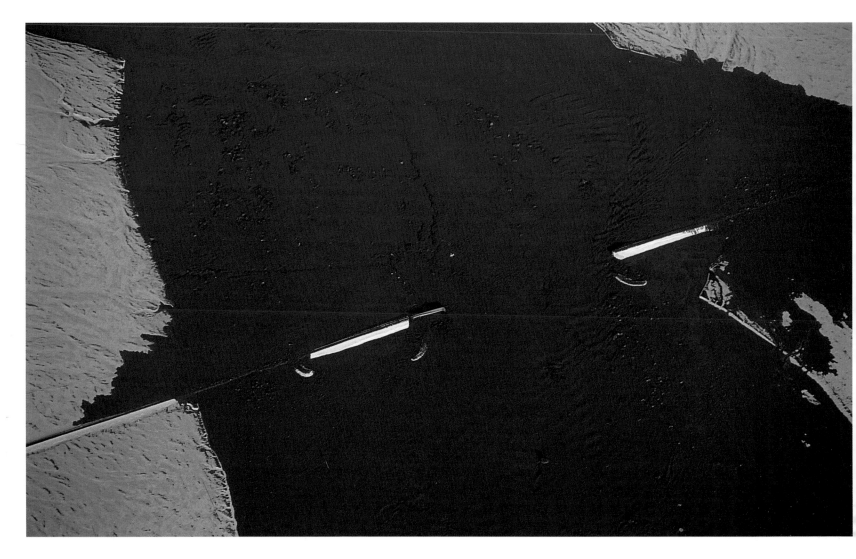

*The road construction authorities built formidable rock walls to protect constructions against inevitable glacial bursts. The bridges over Gígja and Sæluhúsakvísl were entirely destroyed, as were large sections of the road. That matters turned out better than most people imagined at first was partly due to the precautionary measures taken and the strength of the main bridge.*

from a dike leading off from the magma chamber under Bárðarbunga.

## 11. WAITING FOR THE GREAT GLACIAL BURST

Seventeen days later, around October 15th, the eruption was nearly over and Grímsvötn was filled to the brim with water. The first 3 kilometres of the water channel leading from the eruption site had created a huge ice gorge, 200-500 metres broad and nearly 150 metres deep, filled with a continual but decreasing flow of water carrying chunks of ice, blackened by tephra, and containing dissolved gases emitted during the eruption. In the broad and heavily scored ice cauldron

Electrical powerlines, part of the nationwide system, were soon torn down by the flood. Skeiðarjökull and Öræfajökull in the background.

one could see the lip of the smoking crater. Low black islands of sand rose out of the water – representing the summit of a mountainous pile of ash and pillow lava which stands 300 metres above the old tuff ridge from 1938. The new subglacial mountain is one of three such formations created by the eruption, which have a combined volume of 500-700 million cubic metres. This eruption thus became the fourth largest in Iceland this century. When the small team of four men stepped out onto one of the islands formed during the eruption on October 4th, it was minus 19 degrees Celsius and the flow into Grímsvötn had a discharge of about 100-200 cubic metres per second. Grímsvötn had risen by over 140 metres and the ice shelf lay at over 1,500 metres above sea level.

*The glacial burst reached the River Núpsvötn in the west late in the afternoon of November 5. The bridge over Núpsvötn withstood the pressure. Here, people inspect the riverbed of Gígja where the road and a long bridge were swept away. The road is made passable again by December 1996.*

## 12. TREMENDOUS FLOODS

Thirty eight days after the eruption began, came the long awaited glacial burst–at 8:30 in the morning of October 5th. On the previous evening, seismographs had shown that the ice dam in the eastern corner of Grímsvötn had lifted and that it took the water about 10 hours, at a rate of 5 kilometres per hour, to reach the margin of the Skeiðarárjökull outlet glacier. The scientists monitoring the discharge of the Skeiðará River and a policeman from Vík just managed to leave Skeiðarársandur before large parts of it disappeared under a deluge of black and muddy floodwater which managed to double the rate of dis-

*M*ost of the icebergs that floated or rolled onto Skeiðarársandur broke from the Skeiðaárjökull glacier margin in the four pathways of the flood. Many pieces weighed 10-200 tons but large quantities of ice debris followed as well as gigantic chunks, some of them over 1,000 tons in weight.

41

*Between the rivers Skeiðará and Gígja the national highway was badly damaged. The water flowed over it during the early stage of the burst, carrying rocks and ice along with it. Most of the Skeiðará Bridge (906 m) withstood the flood. The support pillars of the bridge were set 10-15 m down into the sand.*

charge recorded in April 1996 in a matter of minutes. By noon the electric and light cables across the sands were destroyed, as was the road itself. The glacial burst first issued from the ice cap at the source of the River Skeiðará, then at Sæluhúsakvísl and finally at the River Gígja. The bridges over the two last named rivers were destroyed in no time. The boulder walls that protected the service centre at Skaftafell held while the 906 metre long bridge over the River Skeiðará, standing soli-

tary above the deluge, began to tremble. First the ends of the bridge, then a part of the bridge itself, disappeared and one of the support columns gave way on the western side. By approximately 17:00, the total discharge had reached a rate of 32,000 cubic metres per second and the glacial burst had reached the River Núpsvötn to the far west of Skeiðarár-sandur.

Great icebergs were cast along the paths of

42

he four main streams of the glacial burst, and equally large pieces of glacier ice rolled over in the flood channels and were tossed aside. South of the road, some of the streams of the flood converged and bore amounts of sediment to the sea so vast that it was discoloured for tens of kilometres away from the shore. The beach itself stretched 800 metres farther out into the ocean. In the pitch black of night, the flood was invisible, but rising all the time. The people on both sides of the sands could only hear the thunderous sound of the water gushing its way south. At about 23:00 on the evening of October 5th, the flood was at its peak, its flow rate being approximately 45-50 thousand cubic metres per second. By 10:00 the following morning, the burst was only a quarter of what it had been the night before, and just over a day later it was virtually over. By that time Grímsvötn had emptied itself of at least four cubic kilometres of water. The ice shelf

*The chunks of ice that came from the River Skeiðá were large indeed, as can be seen from the people and vehicles close by them. They will barely have melted 6-12 months after the burst. The sand will be riddled with pits containing soaked clay and sand for a long time. A view into Morsárdalur.*

*The clash between water and ice is nowhere more evident than at the oulet of Gígja. The water flow spewed out from the glacier and cut two circular groves into its margin. An old moraine diverted the flood west at first, digging a deep channel along the bed of the River Gígja.*

*As with other glacial bursts from Skeiðará, the water poured out of Grímsvötn across a notch in the eastern rim of the caldera below Grímsfjall. This time the roof of the channel over the innermost section collapsed and a vast ice gorge was formed.*

ank by 150-160 metres and the roof of the water channel from Grímsvötn beneath the thick ice cap collapsed noisily. A million tons of ice had broken away from the margin of the Skeiðarárjökull glacier.

## 3. WHAT HAPPENS NEXT?

Central volcanoes and their associate fissure swarms are known to erupt repeatedly within a short span of time so one cannot exclude the possibility of further eruptions in the Bárðarbunga area over the next few years, either within the ice cap or beside it. Also, the loading and deloading of the caldera floor at Grímsvötn (which is in fact the roof of a magma chamber) might exert further pressure on the system there. The channels from Grímsvötn and the eruption site will close due to ice flow and the ice dam

*As the evening sun takes its leave of Vatna-jökull and the new gorge at Grímsvötn assumes a pink hue, our pictorial account of the Vatnajökull ice cap comes to an end.*

to the east of Grímsvötn will sink back to its previous position. Water is collecting again in the lake, but will only continue to do so as a result of geothermal activity and of the small discharge from the new volcanic site as long as there are no further eruptions. Actu-

ally, there was a small eruption on October 7th, which emitted steam and tephra, in the southern end of the huge ice gorge, which goes to prove that the kingdom of Vatna-jökull, with its masses of ice and snow remains as unpredictable as ever.

# SELECTED REFERENCES

Commonly indexed by surnames where Th is substituted for Þ. Here, first names are used.
**Jökull** is the magazine of the Iceland Glaciological Society and the Geoscience Society of Iceland,
P.O. Box 5128, 125 Reykjavík, Iceland.

*Ari Trausti Guðmundsson:*
Volcanoes in Iceland. Vaka-Helgafell, Reykjavík, 1996. 136 pp.

Helgi Björnsson, Páll Einarsson: Volcanoes beneath Vatnajökull, Iceland:
Evidence from Radio Echo Sounding, Earthquakes and Jökulhlaups. Jökull, no. 40, 1990.

*Helgi Björnsson:*
Hydrology of Ice Caps in Volcanic Regions. Soc. Sci.
Isl. 45, Reykjavík 1988. 139 pp.

*Magnús T. Guðmundsson:*
The Grímsvötn Caldera, Vatnajökull: Sub-glacial Topography and Structure of Caldera Infill.
Jökull, no. 39, 1989.

*Magnús T. Guðmundsson, Helgi Björnsson:*
Eruptions in Grímsvötn, Vatnajökull, Iceland. Jökull, no. 41, 1991.

*Sigurður Þórarinsson.*
Vötnin stríð. Saga Skeiðarárhlaupa og Grímsvatnagosa.
Bókaútg. Menningarsjóðs, Reykjavík. 254 p.

*Morgunblaðið*
The chief Icelandic daily newspaper, 30.9.-10.11. 1996; various articles
and interviews with scientists

**Ari Trausti Guðmundsson** has written books on Icelandic nature, mountaineering, travel, astronomy and environmental issues for almost two decades. He is a well-known radio and TV personality and participated in numerous expeditions to high mountains and polar regions. Ari Trausti is a geophysicist and lives in Reykjavík, Iceland.

**Ragnar Th. Sigurðsson** has 20 years experience as a photographer, who has always sought to picture Iceland and the Arctic in an artistic and creative way. He is associated with Tony Stone Images Ltd in the UK. Ragnar has worked and travelled with Ari Trausti and they are co-authors of a book on Icelandic glaciers, LIGHT ON ICE (EISVISIONEN in German). Ragnar lives in Kópavogur, Iceland.

A NEW DOCUMENTARY FILM ON VATNAJÖKULL

The film production company, SAGA FILM, is producing a new and exiting 55-min.-long documentary film on the Vatnajökull ice cap which also covers the recent volcanic events. The film will be available in 1998 for screening on TV and as a video cassette (VHS-PAL, SECAM and NTSC) with both English and German narration. The film is introduced and hosted by Ari Trausti Guðmundsson, one of the authors of this book.

*For further information, please contact:*
SAGA FILM, Vatnagarðar 4, 104 Reykjavík, tel. 568-5085 or fax 581-4802.

**VATNAJÖKULL, ICE ON FIRE**
Arctic Books, Kársnesbraut 63
200 Kópavogur, Iceland
Tel. 564-1171 or 587-7780
Fax 564-3422

All photographs are by Ragnar Th. Sigurðsson, except on p. 8, 33, 34, 35 (marked ATG). These four photos are by Ari Trausti Guðmundsson. Cover photo: The eruption in Vatnajökull, October 5th 1996.

English translation: Martin Regal.

ISBN 9979-9275-1-8

Design: Oddi Printing House Ltd.
Printed by Oddi Printing House Ltd, Reykjavík, 1996.